PECULIAR PETS

Chosen by Brian Moses

Illustrated by Peter Allen

MACMILLAN CHILDREN'S BOOKS

First published 2002
by Macmillan Children's Books
a division of Macmillan Publishers Limited
20 New Wharf Road, London N1 9RR
Basingstoke and Oxford
www.panmacmillan.com

Associated companies throughout the world

ISBN 0 330 39151 8

135798642

A CIP catalogue record for this book is available from the British Library.

Printed by Mackays of Chatham plc, Chatham, Kent.

'My Cat's Ghost' by Tim Pointon, first published in *Young Hippo Spooky Poems*, Scholastic 1998
'Bertie the Hamster' by John Coldwell, first published in *Oxford Reading Tree Poetry: More Catkins: Feelings Poems*
Oxford University Press 1995
'The Purpose of Keeping a Tortoise' by Judith Nicholls, first published in *Dragonsfire*,
Faber and Faber 1990

PECULIAR PETS

Brian Moses lives in St Leonards-on-Sea with his wife Anne and their two daughters Karen and Linette. He spends half his time writing at home and the other half performing his poetry in schools and libraries. His own peculiar pets have included a football-playing rabbit (a Spurs supporter, of course), a lovesick tortoise and a squirrel that still calls round each morning for her digestive biscuit!

Peter Allen was a natural choice for illustrating *Peculiar Pets*. Firstly, his house is full with pets of every shape and size. Secondly, they're all odd. Like his goldfish who drinks orange juice, or the rabbit who sleephops, or the dog who can spell his name with alphabetti spaghetti, or his old sheep who loves watching cartoons . . . They were all really chuffed to have their pictures drawn.

Other books in the **TIME FOR A RHYME** series:

MAGNIFICENT MACHINES
poems chosen by John Foster

SPECTACULAR SPOOKS
poems chosen by Brian Moses

FREAKY FAMILIES
poems chosen by David Orme

WACKY WILD ANIMALS
poems chosen by Brian Moses

DANGEROUS DINOSAURS
poems chosen by Brian Moses

Contents

Cool School Pets
Philip Waddell   1

The Car Pet Showroom
Brian Moses   2

The Purpose of Keeping a Tortoise
Judith Nicholls   4

Mouse Laughing
Mary Green   5

Song for Billy the Gerbil
Peggy Poole   6

Do Goldfish Get Dizzy?
Andrew Collett   7

Pet Food
Richard Caley   8

Bertie the Hamster
John Coldwell   9

Animal Kennings
Michaela Morgan   10

Two Little Budgies
Tony Mitton   11

Big Fat Budgie
Michaela Morgan   12

Goldie
Tony Mitton   13

An Afternoon with Semolina
Frances Nagle   14

Thumper's Den
Tony Mitton   15

Our Hamster's Life
Kit Wright   16

My Rabbit
June Crebbin   19

Hamish the Hamster
Tony Mitton   20

My Stick Insect
Clare Bevan   21

A Protest about Cabbage
Brian Moses   22

Pet Food
David Whitehead   24

My Cat's Ghost
Tim Pointon   26

Supersonic Snail
Clive Webster   27

Walkies
Roger Stevens   28

My Fierce Hamster
Marian Swinger   29

You're Never Alone with a Worm
David Harmer   30

My Bugs
Andrea Shavick   32

Buzz-z-z-z!
Hilary Tinsley   33

Now You See Him, Now You Don't
Mike Johnson   34

Ace Pet
Patricia Leighton   35

Tina
Mike Jubb   36

Number One Room-mate
Patricia Leighton   38

Walking with My Iguana
Brian Moses   40

Dog Talk
Eric Finney   43

Vet Required: Apply Within
Bernard Young   44

No Angel
Sue Cowling   46

Tiny Elephants
Tony Mitton   00

My Pet Bear
Andrew Collett   48

A Real Cool Pet
Paul Bright   52

Cat March
Peter Dixon   54

I Think My Cat's a Space Cat
Clive Riche   56

Cool School Pets

We like grizzly bears and pythons
Alligators, sewer rats.
We like Komodo dragons
And giant vampire bats.
We like man-eating tigers
And tarantulas are nice –
But what are we allowed to keep?
Gerbils, goldfish, mice!

Philip Waddell

The Car Pet Showroom

Bored on long journeys,
tired of the radio,
then visit my showroom –
I do a really nice line
in car pets.

There's a space in your car
that's just right
for the kind of pet
that I have in mind.

A car pet snake
will keep you on your toes,
keep you alert
make sure you don't doze.

Mice are cute
and can live in your boot,
popping in now and then
when you least expect them.

A scorpion for the front seat
when you leave your car.
What a neat way
to deter car thieves.

A lizard for the glove compartment,
a family of woodlice
make a nice addition
to an unused ashtray.

The possibilities are endless,
you'll never be friendless
with a car pet.

Brian Moses

The Purpose of Keeping a Tortoise

A tortoise
is not a pet I long to keep.
In summer?
All he does is eat and crawl.
In winter?
Hide and sleep!

Judith Nicholls

Mouse Laughing

Have you ever heard Mouse laugh?
You'd be surprised.
It doesn't sound as you'd suppose.
No it doesn't.
No squeaks, no twitterings,
No pussy-footing around.
More of a belly laugh, really.
Like the trumpeting howl of an elephant
Thudding across the parched plains of Africa,
Or the deep-throated rumble of the earth
At its centre.
You needn't believe me, of course.
But, next time you meet Mouse,
Don't tickle him.

Mary Green

Song for Billy the Gerbil

Gerbilly, gerbilly, gerbilly mine
rushing around on that wheel all the time,
stopping to make your coat look just fine,
pushing bedding about in some daft design
as if someone might be coming to dine;
you never shout and you never whine
I think you are unusually fine!

Peggy Poole

Do Goldfish Get Dizzy?

My goldfish never stops to rest
she always looks quite busy,
so as she swims around her bowl,
I wonder – is she dizzy?

Andrew Collett

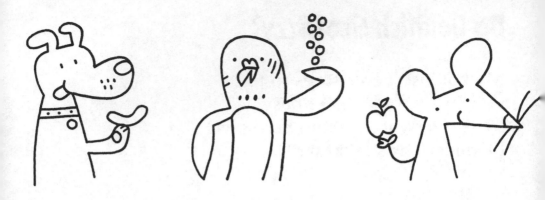

Pet Food

The doggy ate his juicy meat
The budgie ate her seeds
The white mouse nibbled an apple
The rabbit chewed his weeds
The goldfish ate their fishy flakes
The hamster gnawed on a carrot
And by the smile on pussy's face
I think he ate the parrot.

Richard Caley

Bertie the Hamster

Every Sunday I clean Bertie's cage.
I tip his bedding into the bin,
I give his food to the bird,
I pour his water down the sink.

But today there is no Bertie to put back.
Dad says that he had a good life
And two is very old for a hamster.
I look into his empty cage
And remember his soft nose,
His warm fur
And his tiny body sitting on my hand.

John Coldwell

Animal Kennings

Swift swimmer
Good gobbler
Chase player
Fast forgetter
Flake eater
Fin flapper
Gold gleamer
Goldfish

Ear scratcher
Rabbit catcher
Tail wagger
Belly sagger
Mud roller
Keen stroller
Nosy parker
Fierce barker!
Dog!

Michaela Morgan

Two Little Budgies

Two little budgies
sitting close together,
one cocks his head
and the other pecks a feather.
One says *chirrup*
and the other says *trill*.
Two little budgies
can't keep still.

Tony Mitton

11

Big Fat Budgie

I'm a big fat budgie,
I don't do a lot.
Might park on my perch.
Might peck in my pot.
Might peek at my mirror.
Might ring my bell.
Might peer through the bars of my fat budgie cell.
Might say "Who's a pretty boy then?"
Might not.
I'm a big fat budgie.
I don't do a lot.

Michaela Morgan

Goldie

Goldie the guinea pig
lives in a hutch.
She sits and she sniffles
but she doesn't *do* much.
I give her food and water.
I change her straw.
But most of all, I love her.
That's what she's for.

Tony Mitton

An Afternoon with Semolina

We're off to see Aunt Julia's
All-singing all-dancing cat.
Mum asked us what we'd like to do
And we said that.

Her name is Semolina,
Her fur is creamy-white,
She's famous for her talent
And practises all night.

(Which does annoy some neighbours
Who let Aunt Julia know,
But she soothes them with free tickets
For Semolina's show.)

We're squashed-up like sardines
In Aunt Julia's living room
Which is packed to the rafters with kids and cats.
Here comes the opening tune.

The audience falls silent . . .
Semolina pirouettes
To centre stage and starts to croon
What's New Pussy Cat?

Frances Nagle

Thumper's Den

Thumper, my rabbit,
is digging a den.
He burrows down deep
then he comes up again.
He scrabbles his paws
as he scrapes out the earth.
Thumper is digging
for all that he's worth.

Tony Mitton

Our Hamster's Life

Our hamster's life:
there's not much
to it,
not much
to it.

He presses his pink nose
to the door of his cage
and decides for the fifty-six
millionth time
that he can't get
through it.

Our hamster's life:
there's not much
to it,
not much
to it.

It's about the most boring
life in the world,
if he only
knew it.
He sleeps and he drinks and he eats.
He eats and he drinks and he sleeps.

He slinks and he dreeps.
He eats.

This process
he repeats.

Our hamster's life:
there's not much
to it,
not much
to it.

You'd think it would drive him bonkers,
going round and round on his wheel.
It's certainly driving me bonkers,

watching him
do it.

But he may be thinking:
"That boy's life,
there's not much
to it,
not much
to it:

watching a hamster go round on a wheel.
It's driving me bonkers if he only knew it,

watching him
watching me
do it."

Kit Wright

My Rabbit

When my rabbit
is out in his run,

he digs up the ground
like a dog,

washes himself
like a squirrel,

sits on his back legs
like a kangaroo,

leaps and twirls
like an acrobat,

but

when he eats a cabbage leaf,
as is his daily habit,
he delicately nibbles it
EXACTLY like a rabbit!

June Crebbin

Hamish the Hamster

There's a scrabble and a scratch.
There's a scuffle and a squeal.
It's Hamish the Hamster on his
exercise wheel.

There's a nibble and a gnaw.
There's a crackle and a crunch.
It's hungry little Hamish
chewing up his lunch.

Tony Mitton

My Stick Insect

It's brown as a stick
It's thin as a stick,
It grips me with small, sticky feet.
It's still as a stick,
It's stiff as a stick,
And privet is all it will eat.

It casts off its skin
Like a dry, shrivelled twin,
Then just hangs around for a week,
When all's said and done
It isn't much fun –
But it DOES like to play Hide and Seek.

Clare Bevan

A Protest about Cabbage

Our guinea pigs are making
a protest about cabbage.

Each evening we feed them cabbage
but the cabbage stays uneaten.

They know they can outsmart us,
they have started their campaign:

OK, *when they put us in our run,*
eat as much grass as you can stomach,
fill up with enough to last,
then when they throw in the cabbage,
sit tight, we're on a hunger strike.

Well actually they don't really say it like that,
they use guinea pig speak:

Squeak, squeak, squeak, squeak grass,
Squeak, squeak, squeak, squeak lovely.
Squeak, squeak, squeak, squeak cabbage
Squeak, squeak, squeak, squeak YUK!

Pretty soon we'll stop giving them cabbage
and they know it.

Lettuce and carrot are both OK
but they swoon at the thought of grass.
Grass to a guinea pig is
angel delight
strawberries and cream,
Black Forest gateaux,
and Death by Chocolate.

But when I tried it – BIG DISAPPOINTMENT!

I don't know what they see in grass,
but I know what they mean about cabbage!

Don't you?

Brian Moses

Pet Food

I'm looking for some pet food
I'm in the proper row –
Please help me, Mr Sainsbury,
And show me where to go!
I've found lots of bone-shaped biscuits
To put in doggie dishes.
There's millet for your budgies
And ants eggs for your fishes.

Look! Peanuts for the blue-tits
And luxury meat for puppies.
There's grub for gerbils, guinea pigs,
Tropical fish and guppies –
Meaty chews and chocolate drops
To feed to pampered poodles,
And over here for kittens, there's
Chicken-flavoured noodles.

I've read all the pet-food labels
And looked at all the packs.
I've asked the kneeling ladies
Who are filling up the racks.

I've got an empty trolley
And I'm out here in the street,
Please! Help me Mr Sainsbury!

My *Elephant's* got to eat!!

David Whitehead

My Cat's Ghost

There *are* cat ghosts.

Once, I had a ginger and white cat
who used to wake me with his whiskers
and jump for butterflies
in the summer sun.
Now he is dead –
but sometimes I still see him,
out of the corner of my eye,
my ginger and white cat,
ghosting around doorways,
like a memory.

Tim Pointon

Supersonic Snail

I've got a pet snail
That I keep in the shed,
He's really and truly
A sleek thoroughbred.

He's fit as a fiddle
And strong as an ox
And he practises press-ups
Each day in his box.

He holds the world record
For running a metre –
It took him a week
But he's still a world-beater.

He scorches the ground
With his silvery trail,
And he's my little pet –
My own jet-propelled snail.

Clive Webster

Walkies

Walking Zippy
is never nippy –
it takes an hour or so
to walk to the end
of the road and back
because tortoises are so slow.

Roger Stevens

My Fierce Hamster

There goes Herbie, cross and brown,
the fiercest hamster in our town.
Don't poke your finger through his bars.
I did, and I've still got the scars.
He's cuddly, furry, fat and round,
but watch out when those teeth are ground.
Don't try to pick him up, he'll bite.
He's always ready for a fight
and every single day I wish
instead of him, I'd bought a fish.

Marian Swinger

You're Never Alone with a Worm

My pet is called Wilbur
Wilbur the worm.

I tried teaching him to say
"Who's a pretty worm then?"
He pretended not to hear.
I went to take him for a walk
But he slipped away
Down a hole in the garden.

I threw him a stick
And then a ball, no good
He wouldn't fetch them.

I got a bit cross with Wilbur.
"You're a useless pet," I shouted.
But guess what?

He rolled over on his back
Curled up into a wriggly line
Let me stroke his tummy.

He might not be like other pets
But he's very friendly.

David Harmer

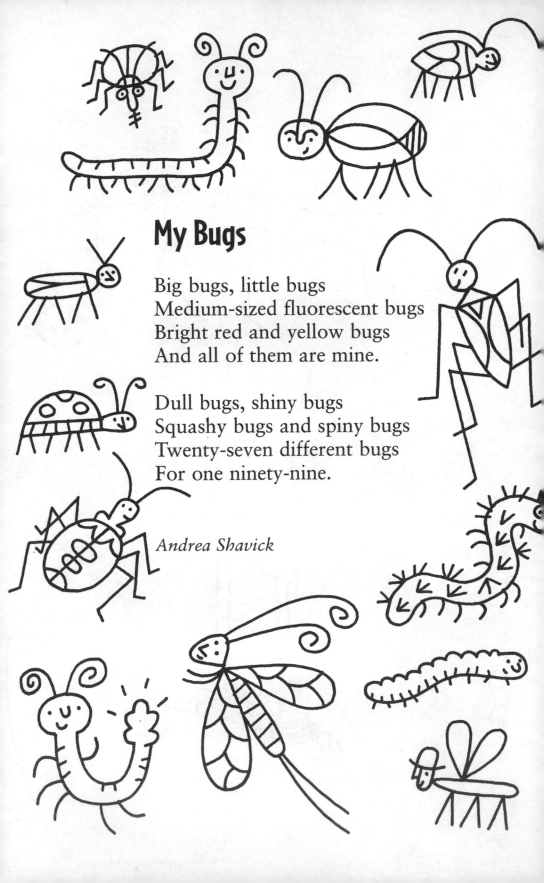

My Bugs

Big bugs, little bugs
Medium-sized fluorescent bugs
Bright red and yellow bugs
And all of them are mine.

Dull bugs, shiny bugs
Squashy bugs and spiny bugs
Twenty-seven different bugs
For one ninety-nine.

Andrea Shavick

BUZZ-Z-Z-Z!

A fly may be an unusual pet
But this one chose to stay,
He moved in during the autumn
And stayed till the following May.

At first Mum tried to swat him
But he was too fast for that,
He avoided the spray and the paper
And flew too high for the cat.

He buzzed about quite happily,
We loved to have him there,
We called him Aristotle
And gave him crumbs to share.

But sad to say when springtime came
The end was plain to see –
We discovered Aristotle, drowned,
In Grandma's cup of tea.

Hilary Tinsley

Now You See Him, Now You Don't

My brother's pet's invisible . . .
Yes, it's as I feared;
the *THING* has gone and gobbled him.
Oh dear, he's disappeared.

Mike Johnson

Ace Pet

Guess what
Jason Archer's got –
a red-kneed tarantula.
I mean – a tarantula
for a pet's pretty keen
but one with RED KNEES?
WOW!

Patricia Leighton

Tina

It was the only time I've ever heard Dad scream.

Of course,
we all *knew* that he hated spiders, and
he never wanted me to have one in the *first* place,

but Mum said
she once had a pet spider
(when she was young)
and she couldn't see any reason
why *I* shouldn't have one too.

Anyway, Tina isn't a very big tarantula.

I can't imagine *how* she could have escaped.
Or how she managed to get all the way
to Dad's bedroom.

Anyway, Dad shouldn't still have been in bed
at that time of day.

Of course,
it was worse because *he* thought
that it was Mum
who was tickling his nose.

Dad doesn't shout much usually.
But boy, can he S C R E A M !

Mike Jubb

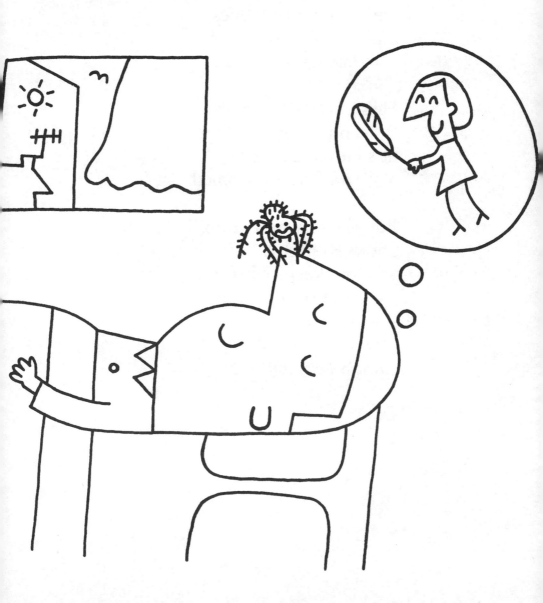

Number One Room-mate

Rupert the Rat
is the best pet I've had,
Rupert is tops
not a doubt.

He's white, soft and silky
with shiny black eyes
and a slinky pink
        string of a tail.

He's not really smelly
(I keep him cleaned out)
he's clever, he's quick
        and well-groomed.

But the very best thing
about Rupert is . . .
        he keeps Mum
        out of my room!

Patricia Leighton

Walking with My Iguana

*(Words in brackets to be repeated by
another voice or voices)*

I'm walking (I'm walking)
with my iguana (with my iguana)

I'm walking (I'm walking)
with my iguana (with my iguana)

When the temperature rises
to above eighty-five,
my iguana is looking
like he's coming alive.

So we make it to the beach,
my iguana and me,
then he sits on my shoulder
as we stroll by the sea . . .

I'm walking (I'm walking)
with my iguana (with my iguana)

I'm walking (I'm walking)
with my iguana (with my iguana)

Well if anyone sees us
we're a big surprise,
my iguana and me
on our daily exercise,

till somebody phones
the local police
and says I have an alligator
tied to a leash.

I'm walking (I'm walking)
with my iguana (with my iguana)

I'm walking (I'm walking)
with my iguana (with my iguana)

It's the spines on his back
that make him look grim,
but he just loves to be tickled
under his chin.

And my iguana will tell me
that he's ready for bed
when he puts on his pyjamas
and lays down his sleepy (Yawn) head.

I'm walking (I'm walking)
with my iguana (with my iguana)

I'm walking (I'm walking)
with my iguana (with my iguana)

With my iguana . . .

Brian Moses

Dog Talk

"Don't go trotting past so fast.
Can't you stop here for a talk?"

"No, sorry. As you see, I'm taking
My pet person for a walk."

Eric Finney

Vet Required: Apply Within

My pet is a monster,
a monster is my pet,
and one day I decided
that he should see the vet.

The vet said, "What's the problem,
is he off his food?"
I said, "No, his appetite is monstrous,
mega, amazing, you'd . . ."

"Open wide," said the vet.

". . . be shocked at what he guzzles;
cardboard, carpets, cassettes.
He eats absolutely everything,
even . . . oh dear . . . vets!"

Bernard Young

No Angel

Angel fish?
No, I don't think so!
I'm a thug
In grey and black.
I'm the bully
Of the fish tank.
I'm the leader –
YOU'RE the pack!

If you bug me
You'll regret it –
Just remember
Who I am.
Nips and nudges,
Shunts and shoves
Are all you'll get
From me, so SCRAM!

Sometimes, though,
When you're enjoying
Such a jolly
Game of tig
Round and round
The sunken ship
I'm sorry that
I'm bad and BIG!

Sue Cowling

Tiny Elephants

I've got elephants,
tiny little elephants,
hardly any bigger
than an ant
or a bee.

I've got elephants,
tiny little elephants.
And every single elephant
belongs to me.

I've got elephants,
tiny little elephants,
peeping from my pockets,
and hiding in my hair.

I've got elephants,
but nobody can see them.
I'm the only person
who knows they're there.

Tony Mitton

My Pet Bear

The bear in my bedroom
is kept as a pet,
even though Dad
hasn't found it, as yet.

He does sometimes wonder
why I've started to roar,
and the reason behind
the holes in my door.

He did look quite worried
his face turned bright pink,
when the hairs from my bear
blocked up the sink.

But he hasn't a clue
he couldn't ever guess,
the real reason behind
my room and its mess.

Andrew Collett

A Real Cool Pet

Anyone there
Want a real cool pet?
Well I'm the one for you, no sweat.

Take me to bed
Take me to school
I'll stick by you and I'll stay real cool.

I don't bark,
Miaow or squawk
Won't even notice it when I talk.

Always find me
Without fail
Need no detective to follow my trail.

Food's no problem
I don't make scenes
Never been known to leave my greens.

Need no brushing
Got no hair
But you can tickle me anywhere.

Never argue
Just obey
See what happens when you tell me "Stay!"

Some want a bird
Some want a bug
So surely somebody wants a slug?
There must be somebody who wants a slug?

Paul Bright

Cat March

He's on my bed
again

                                next to my ear.
He is purring
he is marching
        left foot up
        right foot down
        left foot down
        right foot up.

I ask Mum why he is marching
and
why he is purring . . .
Mum says it's what cats do.
I ask Mum where
he is going.
She says nowhere
but I know where he is going
                if
        he does not pack it in.

Peter Dixon

I Think My Cat's a Space Cat

I think my cat's a space cat.
She goes to the moon at night.
She takes the shimmer from the stars,
And makes it into light.

On gossamer she floats to earth,
And lands upon my bed.
Her fur brings scent of galaxies
And things the moon has said.

I think my cat's a space cat.
The sun upon her gleams,
Her eyes are green, her face is black,
Her smile in all my dreams.

Clive Riche